THE STORY OF TIGGYWINKLES' FIRST ENCOUN

Red Kites

WORDS AND PHOTOGRAPHY BY LES STOCKER MBE, HON ASSOC RCVS

Matador
9 Priory Business Park
Kibworth Beauchamp
Leicester LE8 0RX, UK
Tel: 0116 279 2299
Fax: 0116 279 2277
Email: books@troubador.co.uk
Web: www.troubador.co.uk/matador

Designed by Emily Godwin
www.emilygodwin.co.uk

Many thanks to Lucy Thrift for typing my manuscript
Jane Greenwood for proof reading the final copies

Photographs by Les Stocker

ISBN 9781780880396

British Library Cataloguing in Publication Data.
A catalogue record for this book is available from the British Library.

Matador is an imprint of Troubador Publishing Ltd

Dedicated to all the Red Kites
that magic the sky over
the Chiltern Hills

THE STORY OF TIGGYWINKLES' FIRST ENCOUNTERS WITH

Red Kites

WORDS AND PHOTOGRAPHY BY LES STOCKER MBE, HON ASSOC RCVS

Tiggywinkles started life as a wildlife rescue centre way back in 1978. At the time there seemed to be no care available or care at all for sick, injured or displaced wild birds and other animals. Sue, Les and Colin Stocker seeing this enormous black hole in Britain's concern for its wildlife opened their doors and arms to any wild creature that was in trouble.

Initially there were few; a tawny owl, a wood pigeon and, of course, a ubiquitous blackbird; the first of many thousands to be taken in over the next thirty years. In those days there were no large birds of prey in the area. Tiggywinkles perfected its own techniques, there was no reference material, on sparrowhawks, hobbies, a merlin and, that most special of birds, the kestrel. Owls were regular patients and even a giant snowy owl that had escaped its prison in Oxford. One peregrine every five years but never a sign of a buzzard or a red kite.

Gradually in the early nineties buzzards started to occur and settle in the Chilterns. We knew every family and could identify each of the few patients. Up in the hills the red kite re-introduction programme was up and running. But there were so few it was surely a good thing that we never saw a casualty. We often wondered, at the time, if our experience could cope with such a bird.

112

(Above) In the early nineties buzzards started to occur and settle in the Chiltern hills.

(Right) Kestrels, like this youngster, used to be the most common bird of prey before red kites joined them in their aerial antics.

'It was generally on its last legs. The priority was to get fluids into the kite, as its severe dehydration was about to kill it.'

Then it happened in 1998 a live bird, baby red kite was brought in by the re-introduction team. While monitoring that year's nest this bird had been found grossly disfigured and obviously in serious trouble. Thankfully our full, well tried and tested, first aid programme slid into action. The kite had a terribly swollen head. Its mouth was completely blocked by a cheesy growth and it was generally on its last legs. The priority was to get fluids into the kite, as its severe dehydration was about to kill it. A lubricated tube was slid past the mass and down its throat into its proventriculus just above its gizzard, its stomach facility. Carefully, so as not to drown it, isotonic rehydration fluid was passed into its system. Then keeping her, we think it was a female, upright we set to tackle that mass that was threatening to kill her.

3 | 4

This was a disease called trichomoniasis that manifests itself as minute single celled parasites, flagellate protozoa, invading the tissues of a bird's mouth and throat. Commonly caught from other birds this assault was probably contracted from a carrion bird carcass fed to it by its parents. So deeply embedded are these infections that they cannot simply be removed. To try to remove them without treatment would result in massive uncontrollable bleeding. However a special medication will kill off the protozoans and gradually over a week or two the mass will fall away revealing healthy tissue underneath. A broad cover of antibiotics would also counteract any secondary bacterial infection.

(Top and bottom left) Phoebe was terribly infected and disfigured by trichomoniasis when she was brought into us. Pulling out all the stops she recovered and although not the prettiest of red kites she has been for many years a solid part of Tiggys' family.

(Left) Phoebe sits proud in her aviary.

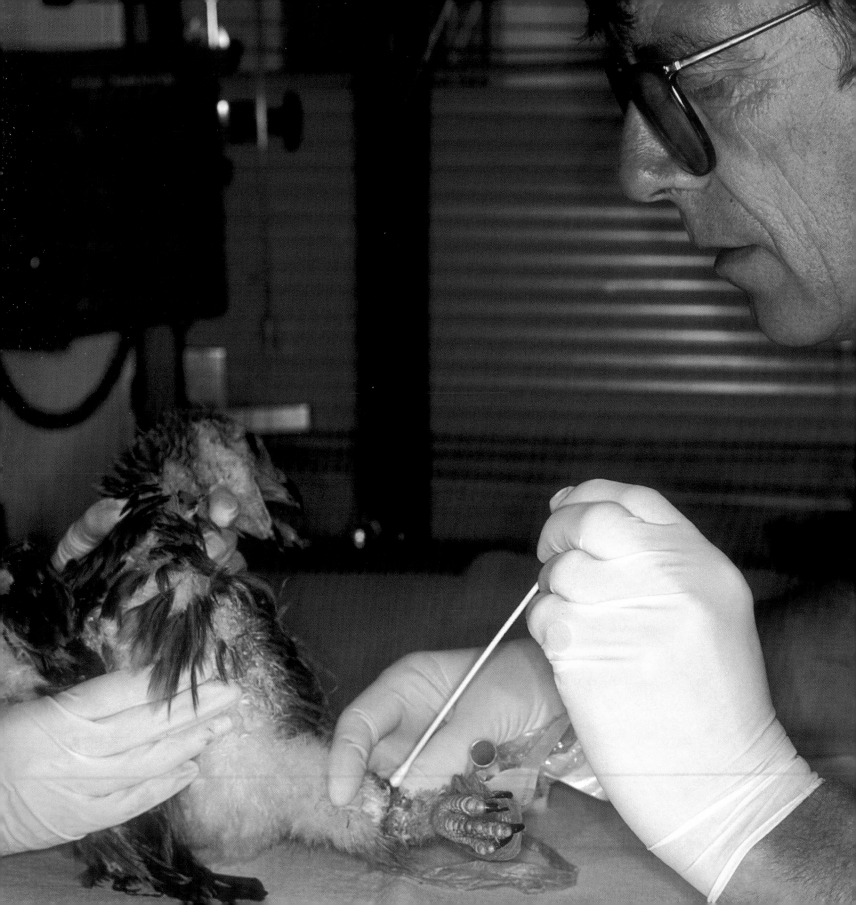

Sadly although we saved the bird's life and cleared the trichomoniasis the mass falling away from the roof of the mouth included the top beak. There are no techniques, even at Tiggywinkles, to repair or replace a kite's top beak. We knew this and decided then that this kite could never be released and would have to be hand fed. However we were going to provide all its requirements throughout its life including a mate if it all worked out. Phoebe has now been with us for over twelve years still demanding her food at feeding time but very much a totally loved member of Tiggys' exclusive family of resident animals.

Phoebe's was a natural affliction however our next red kite casualty, another nestling found by the kite group had fallen foul of man's world. This kite's parents had diligently built a nest of twigs, leaves, in fact anything they could use. Horrifically they had also included, that blight on the countryside, a discarded plastic bag. This young kite now had the plastic bag wrapped around and embedded into its leg just like a tourniquet. Left in place the structure would have eventually cut deeper into the leg with the lower part dying and falling off. Removing a ligature like this one can cause bleeding but we removed it carefully and cleaned and treated the wound left behind. This kite did recover very quickly and we arranged with the kite group for it to be returned to its nest after any further rubbish had been removed.

5 | 6

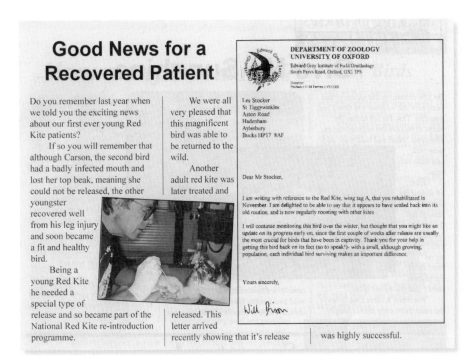

Good News for a Recovered Patient

Do you remember last year when we told you the exciting news about our first ever young Red Kite patients?

If so you will remember that although Carson, the second bird had a badly infected mouth and lost her top beak, meaning she could not be released, the other youngster recovered well from his leg injury and soon became a fit and healthy bird.

Being a young Red Kite he needed a special type of release and so became part of the National Red Kite re-introduction programme.

We were all very pleased that this magnificent bird was able to be returned to the wild.

Another adult red kite was later treated and released. This letter arrived recently showing that it's release

was highly successful.

DEPARTMENT OF ZOOLOGY
UNIVERSITY OF OXFORD
Edward Grey Institute of Field Ornithology
South Parks Road, Oxford, OX1 3PS

Director:
Professor C M Perrins LVO FRS

Les Stocker
St Tiggywinkles
Aston Road
Hadenham
Aylesbury
Bucks HP17 8AF

Dear Mr Stocker,

I am writing with reference to the Red Kite, wing tag A, that you rehabilitated in November. I am delighted to be able to say that it appears to have settled back into its old routine, and is now regularly roosting with other kites

I will continue monitoring this bird over the winter, but thought that you might like an update on its progress early on, since the first couple of weeks after release are usually the most crucial for birds that have been in captivity. Thank you for your help in getting this bird back on its feet (so to speak) - with a small, although growing, population, each individual bird surviving makes an important difference.

Yours sincerely,

Will Bixon

(Left) Removing the ligature from the young kite's leg demanded massive concentration and delicate cleaning of the wound.

Looking grumpy this young kite can't wait to be back in its nest.

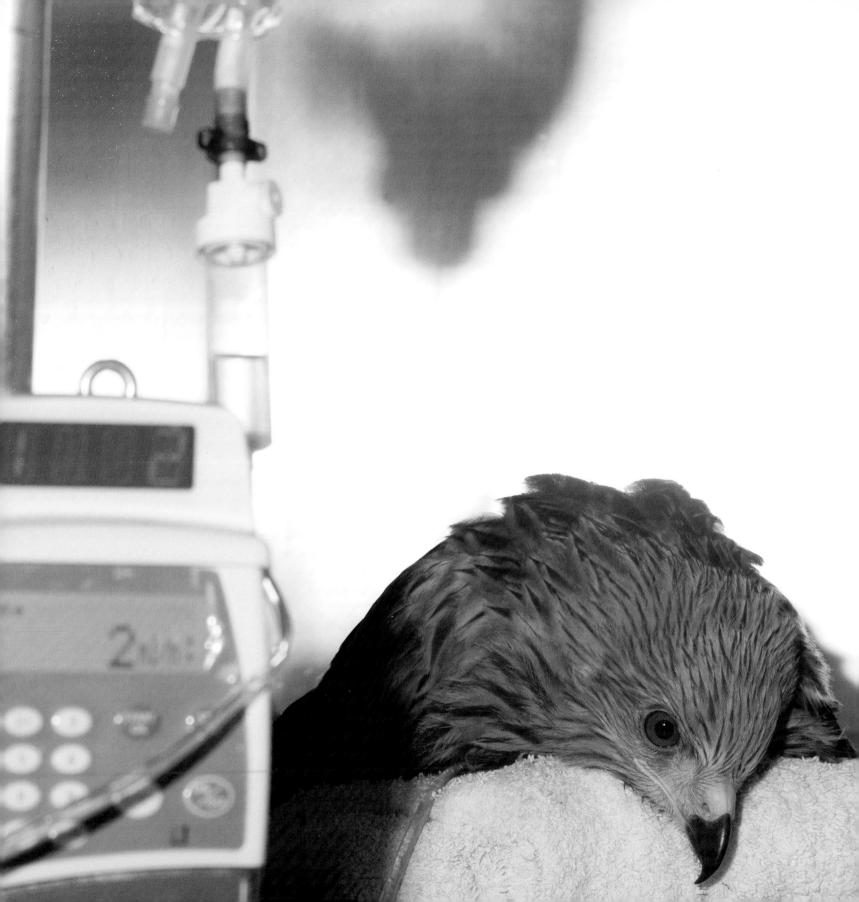

'There was very little written information and no veterinary training on wild bird fractures so innovation and technique has enabled us to recognise and treat most casualties.'

Being in the Chilterns, with a high red kite population, it is not unusual to see them feeding on road casualties. This is a perilous lifestyle with many kites getting hit by cars. However thankfully most seem to escape by the 'skin of their teeth' if they had any. The unwary and unlucky casualties are found and brought to us appearing to be badly injured and even comatose. We know these birds, how they choose to 'play dead', lying flat on the floor and, in most cases, allowing themselves to be picked up. We take all the precautions, knowing they can be quite dangerous, but carry on with the full first aid and lifesaving protocol including, as they are larger birds, intravenous therapy and pain relief. When they think that they are not being watched they will suddenly spring into life and stand up. Then we can take a cursory opinion of any injuries. A hanging wing can mean there is a fracture of one of the fragile long bones that make red kites so magnificently aerodynamic. Still Tiggywinkles are fully experienced in dealing with fractures in birds. Hundreds, every year, pass through the bird fracture clinic with most recovering back to the wild.

9 | 10

There was very little written information and no veterinary training on wild bird fractures so innovation and technique has enabled us to recognise and treat most casualties. Splinting or plastering fractures in birds is not suitable because of the weight and of trapping infection, as many of the fractures are compound and open to contamination. At Tiggywinkles' our vets favour using hollow stainless steel pins in various ways including intramedullary pinning, extracutaneous fixation and external fixators using stainless steel traction systems. Bird fractures, with antibiotic treatment and sturdy fixation will usually heal within weeks. A period of convalescence, physiotherapy and exercise, in our new red kite aviary complex, should see the bird released as soon as suitable.

(Above) The subtle drop of this kite's right wing may mean there is a problem with it.

(Left) Red kite casualties that are seriously injured, like this patient may need intravenous fluid therapy with its head supported on towels.

A red kite's long bones of the wings and legs have to be strong yet also be very lightweight. They are hollow and thin and are broken very easily. Not only are they broken very easily but also the bird will continue trying to use that limb causing even more damage as it panics. They are brought into Tiggys with broken bones pointing in all directions and, more often than not, poking through torn skin allowing deadly infection into the wound. On admittance the damaged limb is temporarily strapped up to prevent any further damage. The kite will then receive its standard first aid and lifesaving and be settled into Intensive Care. Within 24 hours the fractured limb is x-rayed and formally stabilised by the vet.

Over the years Tiggywinkles' has dealt with literally thousands of birds with major fractures. Tiggys' has perfected its' own techniques to repair bird fractures using a strong yet lightweight system called 'extra-cutaneous fixation'. Initially any long bone that is fractured has an intramedullary pin, a sterile stainless steel needle, inserted in the fragments of hollow bone holding it to its original shape. Then four much smaller stainless steel needles are passed transversely through the bone fragments, two on each side of any fracture. These are locked together on both sides of the limb to hold it rigid. At first a Tiggywinkles' designed splint is origamied from the best splinting material, Weetabix boxes, then wrapped around the limb to prevent any rotation of the fracture. The splint will also be removed after five days along with the intramedullary pin. About two to three weeks later the bones should be held by a formed callus so that all the metalwork can be removed. Then after a period of convalescence, exercise and feather growth our kite should be fit to go back to the wild.

11 | 12

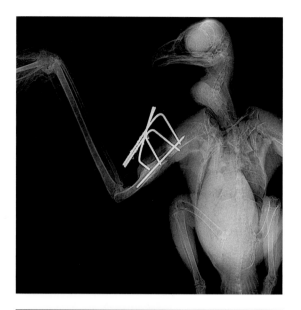

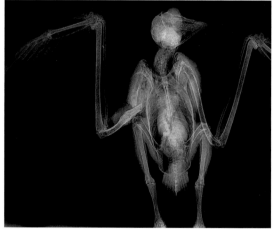

(Above) Typical x-rays allowing the latest innovative techniques to be used to treat red kite casualties.

(Right) There is nothing more glorious in Britain's countryside than a fully recovered red kite in its wild element.

Not all our red kite casualties are majestic full size birds. One kite that was brought in was a ball of white fluff, all beak, eyes and attitude for such a little 'big' baby. Not for this little guy the 'playing dead' ploy of its adult kites, instead a white ball of fury, talons up and ready to attack any unwary hand. At first our nursery team cut up raw meat, fur and feathers to hand feed him. Before long he quickly got the hang of tearing his own food up. Naturally he took more meat than ever and started to grow and grow. Before long he had the full red kite regalia with just a few tufts of fluffy down showing that he was still very much a youngster.

In our nurseries we have a make sure that all hand-rearing of all species follows regimented guidelines. All animals, including birds, can become 'imprinted', that is habituated to humans. Once afflicted they will probably never become wild. This, of course, defeats the whole 'raison d'etre' for Tiggywinkles; a situation we would regard as a failure. As planned this little red kite remained frighteningly wild and raring to fly. Time in one of our red kite aviaries enabled him to build up his muscle strength and flying expertise. Watching him gaining strength and flying powerfully, yet so deftly, lapping the aviary soon let us know that he was ready to leave. In our red kite complex we have a specially built hatch so that any birds released via its platform know that there is a source of food and shelter they can return to if they get into trouble. Before this complex was built we had to use temporary improvised release hatches to release many species of bird.

13 | 14

And so true to form, through a makeshift hatch, this our first really baby red kite soared up and up into the clouds to where he belonged. Red kites belong in the sky. They are the masters of majestic effort free soaring, calling and scanning below for any morsel, usually carrion. They are relaxed flying over the Chilterns. Nothing to fear only those accidents that do happen. They would not expect a human to deliberately kill them, sending them plummeting to the ground and unlikely to survive.

(Above) It takes many weeks before the chick begins to look anything like an adult.

(Top Left) Red kite chicks hardly ever fall from the nest. This orphaned kite is typically white, fluffy and aggressive.

(Bottom Left) Red kite chicks are quite large and do not 'play dead' like their elders.

One kite in particular was ambushed by some trigger-happy moron. She did survive the impact with the ground but was brought to Tiggywinkles by a good Samaritan who spotted her. And what a special red kite she turned out to be as her life was so nearly snuffed out by that gun. This kite had a numbered wing tag on each wing. We could tell from these markers that the kite, so special, was one of the original pathfinders brought over from Spain in 1991 as part of Britain's re-introduction programme.

15 | 16

For fourteen years she had made the Chiltern Hills her home and now here she was, injured and lying on our operating table. She was supported on an intravenous drip and the gunshot wound cleared of all the broken feathers and other detritus that the gun pellet forces into the wound. It would have taken too much invasive surgery to remove the pellet itself. It would cause no more harm so we left it in situ. An x-ray showed the pellet but thankfully revealed that there were no bone fractures. The wound would heal under antibiotic medication and in fact, after a few weeks, she was released back into her Chiltern Hills. There was never any trace of the perpetrator of this bird's injury but if the same thing ever happens again I am sure that local people would move heaven and earth to track down the potential killer.

(Right) No 5 feeling better and showing his coloured wing tags.

(Left) Les assesses the recovery of the 'special' Red Kite

As you can probably imagine the influx, of red kite casualties, grew and grew. The original aviary facilities we put up in the building of the Hospital never envisaged such large birds needing housing.

17 | 18

In order to get recovered casualty red kites to full fitness for release they have to be able to exercise, fly and manoeuvre. New larger aviaries would provide this space and incidentally let us marvel at a kite's flying prowess.

With the aviary built, it soon became obvious that even this giant aviary would be overflowing with recoupees. We knew then that more giant aviaries would soon be needed.

(Above) The tremendous size of the aviaries allows red kites, massive birds, to exercise their flying prowess before they are fit for release.

(Right) Bright Ideas issue 39

Space - The Ultimate Frontier

When we first built the Hospital in 1991, the largest birds of prey we ever treated were kestrels and tawny owls. The aviaries we designed and built for their convalescence and exercise before release were at the time, quite substantial and adequate for all their needs.

But in recent years the countryside around the Hospital has changed and we are now seeing much larger buzzards and those glories of the sky, red kites. Until now we, and they, have had to make do with the original aviaries, large though they were.

And then along came Phoebe, the red kite chick, who was suffering from the terrible disease, trichomoniasis. We conquered the disease but it had already eaten away Phoebe's top beak. Even we, who attempt the impossible, can do nothing to substitute a prosthetic beak so from that moment we decided that Phoebe could never be released and should live with us.

Apart from having no top beak Phoebe is a glorious, enormous red kite who, although living on her own, had made friends, not just with all of us, but also the buzzards in the next aviary.

She, and they, demanded something more in keeping with their size, so when the builders were in I asked the carpenter to design

The new aviary

and build an aviary based on using telegraph poles as the uprights.

Lo and behold the design arrived, then the telegraph poles and wire and soon the most spectacular aviary was up and ready for Phoebe and Co. Extra long perches were provided by cut outs from the nearby Forestry Commission and with them in place Phoebe, first, and then the buzzards, were taken down and let loose in the new home.

At first all were a little agrophobic but soon the buzzards were calling and clamouring over the long perches. Phoebe, after a few days flew for the first time, from one end to the other landing clumsily with her new found freedom.

With all the space we are seeing a marked improvement in the recuperation of some of the buzzards and rumour now has it that we are saving up to build another gargantuan alongside this success.

Phoebe perched inside the new aviary learning to cope with the space

www.sttiggywinkles.org.uk

Unfortunately red kites in their high speed 'stoops' towards food on the ground do make mistakes. At phenomenal speed they try to negotiate barbed wire fences or thick thorny hedgerows. They fail to see a hazard and get tangled, unable to escape. Naturally they panic and flap frantically trying to free themselves. This inevitably causes all sorts of skin and tissue damage making our handling of the wounds, after they have been rescued, a delicate and patient process.

In many cases they will have damaged the metacarpus, the very tip of the wing so vital in manoeuvring whilst flying. This part of the wing has a very meagre blood supply causing the wing tip to die off if it is compromised in any way. Kites with wing tip injuries are immediately put on an intravenous drip and drugs to bolster their circulation to keep tiny blood vessels viable. Damage to the metacarpus is probably our worst nightmare when it comes to injuries to birds. The circulatory damage is bad enough but a worse condition, often caused by getting trapped or collision is 'wing tip oedema'. The whole area of the metacarpus and even the carpal joint, the wrist, become horribly bloated, inflamed tissue full of fluid. The swelling can compromise the blood supply to the whole area. It can damage the carpal joint, so vital in flying manoeuvres, to the extent that it might fail. Worst of all, the swollen tissues themselves can become infected and the wing tip fail to survive. Treatment, so vital, involves anti-inflammatory drugs and regular massaging of the affected areas with many human medications for similar conditions in people. Red kites generally get caught up in low hazards, such as fences and hedges. However one particular kite decided to break all the rules and get itself trapped at the top of a 60 feet high poplar tree.

(Right and Above top) Red kites making low passes can fall foul of low flying hazards.

(Above) Injury and serious damage to red kite wings can often be caused by collisions with fences.

The whole story was reproduced in our newsletter Bright Eyes in a piece headlined "Where on Earth have you been?" The article is reproduced here:-

The call came in, "There's a bird up a tree. Can you help me?" I knew it was early April but April Fools Day had passed.

"Pull the other one", I chortled.
"No, really there is a red kite stuck 60 feet up a tree in my garden."

Perhaps it wasn't a joke. It was in Chinnor so Joe, who lived there, went to have a look. On site he phoned to say that there was a red kite trapped up a tree, at least 50 feet above the ground. I went to investigate and found that there was, indeed a red kite barely visible, flapping at the top of this enormous, very thin tree. Oh boy! Probably a job for the Fire Brigade, I commandeered the conservatory to make some phone calls. Reaching the regional headquarters of the Fire Brigade I found them reluctant to even come and assess the rescue of the bird. Back in the garden the rescue looked impossible, even if the Fire Brigade had come. I had had to watch a kestrel die at the end of the branches of another giant tree. I didn't want this bird to suffer in the same way.

So we all racked our brains for a solution. Karen, who had originally called the RSPCA who passed the call onto to us, suggested an 'arborist'. Who on earth was that? But she was dead right, through yellow pages we both started phoning the local tree surgeons. It was Bank Holiday Monday but eventually one I phoned said, "I'll ask my climber if he can help." Wow! This guy had a climber. Yes he could help and he and his climber were soon on the scene. Patrick Kernan wasn't perturbed at the flimsiness of the tree and soon had his harness, helmet and equipment on ready to assault the tree.

"Be careful when you reach the bird," I advised. "Its talons can be painful if it attacks you. Wear some gloves."

Off he went. We stood open mouthed as he shimmied up the tree as if it was a climbing frame. At phenomenal speed he was in minutes grappling with the trapped bird. Then he had it and grasping its' legs abseiled down to the ground, dripping blood where he had forgotten to take his gloves up to the canopy. I took the bird. It did not seem any worse for wear but I took it back to Tiggys' just to monitor it for a few days. It seemed fine, so after a few trial flights in one of our large aviaries I decided it could go back to the garden. Once we were back in the garden, Karen told me that the kite did seem to have a mate who had been, for the last two days, flying up and down looking for its other half. Joe, who had first responded to the call, put the kite on the ground and let go. It flew towards the bottom of the garden wall below the height of the fence. We all thought it was going to crash but it flexed it's glorious long wings and ever so slowly flew majestically up and up. Before long it was almost at cloud height no doubt, full of excuses, looking for its' mate, full of excuses.

21 | 22

(Right) Patrick Kernan makes short work of scaling the 60ft tree to rescue the clumsy kite.

(Far right) This time, this kite abseiled to the ground, rescued.

(Above) Feeling better. A juvenile kite, fully recovered and demanding to finally be released.

(Right) Bright Eyes issue 43

The Story of A6

Earlier in the year two red kites made a nest near Stokenchurch. Little did they know that pointing at that nest was a CCTV camera relaying their every action back to a viewing point at a local garden centre.

The pair of kites obliged and layed three eggs which duly hatched. English Nature, the government body majoring on red kites, had the three

ended up being brought to us.

She was not badly injured but could not fly, as we found out when we tried to release her after a few days.

There was no outside indication of a problem but an x-ray showed some bony changes to the carpal joint and ulna of her right wing. Dr John Lewis, our vet, noted

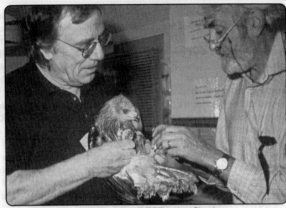

A6 has her DEFRA ring fitted

either testes or ovaries.

John referred the condition of A6 to particular veterinary bird specialists but none could improve on his diagnosis.

As it happens A6 is improving with regular antibiotic therapy although she cannot yet cope with rain and has to be brought inside to dry after every heavy shower. Hopefully her plumage will become weatherproof enabling us

to release her once her wing heals completely.

In the meantime, being a red kite on Schedule 4, of the Wildlife and Countryside Act, A6 has to be registered at a cost of £20, and ringed by DEFRA the government body replacing the old MAFF.

So far A6 is improving and we look forward to re-introducing her, probably through the government re-introduction scheme, back to the wild during next year.

babies weighed, measured, ringed and tagged to add more information to their growing dossier on the red kite re-introduction to Britain.

The smallest of the chicks was labelled (as were the others), with bright yellow identifying wing tags declaring her as A6. She suffered terribly at the feet of her siblings and grew up much more slowly than they did.

Eventually they all flew the nest but A6 only made it as far as Bicester, where she obviously collided with something and

the changes and that an infection, caused by the collision to the carpal joint, had spread down the periosteum of her wing bones causing the weakness.

While she was under that initial examination, John was able, using a tiny endoscope, to internally confirm that A6 was a female. From the outside both sexes of red kites look identical. The only way to establish a gender is with a very minor incursion into the bird's abdomen to confirm

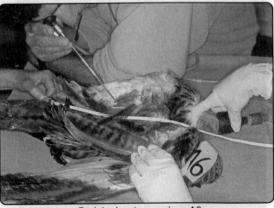

Dr John Lewis examines A6

We never, in our wildest dreams, could have conjured up the horrors that we would meet in the world of red kites. The call we had been dreading for years came. It hit us all between the eyes. This was a call to a red kite lying dead in a wood near Benson in Oxfordshire. Hurrying to the spot there was, indeed, a glorious red kite, lying horribly still and cold under some trees. There was no sign of any injuries so as a matter of course we informed the police of our nightmare call. Their reaction was swift and positive. Apparently in that area another five red kites had been found dead with no signs of injury. They asked for this dead red kite for tests to see if it had been poisoned. This was our first step in the investigation but when we looked further into the place where the bird was found, the truth became dramatically obvious. On the open ground there were rabbit carcasses crucified and fixed to the ground. These appeared to be the poisoned baits to attract the kites and anything else that ventured onto that land.

25 | 26

The whole area was a slaughterhouse with bits of birds all over the place and worse of all a gibbet, a term used by gamekeepers for a fence where they can pathetically, yet terribly display their conquests. This particular fence ran off into the distance and was festooned with hanging dead foxes and crows. The whole area was a callous killing field. There is not much that the law can do about foxes, crows and rabbits being killed. However, the law was aghast at the slaughter of the red kites. Thankfully, the police put through a major criminal prosecution resulting in the landowner and his gamekeeper receiving massive fines and, of course, criminal records.

(Overpage left) Finding this poisoned red kite encouraged us and the police to investigate.

(Overpage right) The horrific sight of this gamekeeper's gibbet was so typical of a countryside 'killing zone'.

BVNA Congress

Yet another abbreviationbut this time a very prestigious organisation the British Veterinary Nursing Association. And why is it mentioned here? Its because Les was accorded the honour of being asked to open the B.V.N.A. Annual Congress held at the National Agricultural Centre at Stoneleigh.

Les's opening address, before a packed auditorium, stressed the part that veterinary nurses have played in getting veterinary practices to treat wildlife. He also reiterated that under the amendment to Schedule 3 of the Veterinary Surgeons Act, veterinary nurses could now officially carry out minor surgical procedures.

Les, Sue and Lisa were guests of the B.V.N.A at the Congress and at the Warwick Hilton overnight which proved to be a very exhilerating weekend for all three of them.

Court Cases

Not many people realise that we assist other agencies in prosecuting those who contravene wildlife laws in this country. These are just a few of our assists:

Informing the police of poisoning a very rare red kite and providing evidence for the resulting prosecution. The guilty party was eventually fined £13,500.

Providing care for rescued crows and post mortems of dead corvids (crows and magpies)trapped negligently. Gamekeeper found guilty.

Attempting to save a hedgehog deliberately set on fire by hooligans. Providing subsequent post mortem and photographs.

Being able to provide information of how a mink hunt decimated a swan's nest and killed two cygnets.

There are other cases pending but as always we shall work with the police and other agencies in their efforts to stamp out wildlife crime and abuse.

The Red Kite Used In Evidence

Is Anyone able to

Of course, all incidents involving red kites are totally serious. True, every red kite that arrives at Tiggywinkles starts a buzz of excitement through everybody. Yet every now and then, as with all other species, a bizarre incident has everybody 'scratching their heads' as to how even a red kite could get itself in such a strange predicament. At Tiggywinkles we are totally prepared when dealing with birds affected by oil. Major disasters have seen our teams mobilised. In fact just recently we installed a bespoke oiled bird washing facility in the area known as 'the swan room'.

Usually there are sea birds, ducks and even swans covered in oil but this bizarre incident brought us a red kite covered in oil. The oil smelt like cooking oil but how on earth did a kite get covered in cooking oil. After a couple of days the kite had recovered from its shock and regained its dignity, although still covered in oil. The oiled bird washing team prepared for the specialised cleaning process. Oiled birds have to be washed at 42°C in a precise 2% solution of Fairy Liquid. This normally works well and after the bird has been totally rinsed, again at 42°C, the feathers should become drier. Works great on ordinary birds but this oil refused to budge off a special bird. After the wash the kite, looking totally waterlogged and bedraggled, still felt oily and greasy. A few days later he was washed again but the oil was still there. We were not going to get this oil off. The only solution was to keep the kite in one of our aviaries until its annual moult had replaced all of its feathers. This would take two to three months but with new clean feathers the kite could safely be released. We never did find out how it had become covered in cooking oil. Stranger than fiction.

29 | 30

(Overpage and left) Washing any bird, covered in oil, is a complicated, very specific and very wet process. The handlers and the bird all lose their dignity in a mass of warm water and Fairy Liquid.

(Above) Dignity restored our oiled kite, looking better, starts his convalescence.

The most wonderful birds

Nurse Abby with one of our patients

There is one great success story of conservation in Britain, that is the re-introduction of the Red Kite to chosen natural areas across the country. At Tiggys we are lucky that one of the most successful areas of re-introduction was on the Chiltern Hills, right on our doorstep.

The Kites fly over us in ones, twos and even more, often trying to partake in the food put out for our Herons and Gulls. As they glide above us and dive down to feed they must be the most spectacular bird in England. At Tiggys every Red Kite that crosses us is "Tannoyed" causing most of the staff and students to stop their chores and wonder at the marvels showing off above us.

However it does seem to me that it is some kind of miracle that they have been so successful. Every year, and especially this year, as the youngsters leave their nests, the weather seems to deteriorate and pour down for days on end. All of a sudden their youngsters can't cope. They seem to get very wet, stop flying and are, if they are lucky, found by passers by wet, cold and very down and out lying, often in deep woodland. Hypothermia is creeping in and soon, if they weren't found, these glorious birds would shiver to death.

The lucky ones are found and brought to us. Once in our care we can put them on warm intravenous drips, dry them off and warm them through. We also wrap their tails in cardboard to stop them getting their feathers damaged while in care. Broken feathers would seriously hamper their chance of release. Thankfully within 24 hours they usually recover enough to stand up so that we can feed them (they are usually starving) on liquid feed, initially, gradually weaning them onto more substantial Kite food.

We let them age a little more. Then once they are fit and the weather improved we slowly release them onto our Chiltern Hills wonderland.

Just a note that if you find any bird cold and wet on the floor dry it off a bit, wrap it in a space blanket and get it, without delay, to a wildlife trauma centre.

Over the last two weeks, during a period of very damp, wet weather, we have already admitted these four Red Kites. Let's hope it improves so no more of these glorious birds have to suffer.

Four Red Kite patients

Perfect feathers are totally crucial for an aerodynamic master like a red kite. At Tiggys we have to take great care that any birds in cages do not damage their flight feathers to any extent. As soon as a kite, or any bird of prey, arrives at the Hospital a sheath, usually fashioned from old x-ray film is fitted over that wonderful avionic forked tail. The tail feathers are the most vulnerable and if they are badly damaged there could be a lengthy delay before they regrow. True the broken feathers can be plucked to encourage regrowth however this is unacceptable as it is painful to the bird and could damage the feather follicle itself.

33 | 34

An alternative, a way of mending broken feathers called 'imping' has proved very successful where only one or just a few main feathers are broken. A piece of any old feather is cut to model a broken feather back into its original length. The feather shafts are hollow allowing a stainless steel needle to be glued into each half. The two parts are pushed together over the glued needle until they touch. The needle stays in place and will fall out when the feather is moulted naturally and replaced.

(Above) Wrapping the tail of a bird of prey keeps its feathers intact allowing it to be quickly released on its recovery.

(Left) Bright Eyes issue 54

Staff members successfully

Jane lunges the first kite into the air

Verity who must be obeyed is next

Trendy Chris

NVQ student Ashleigh

It's curly Chris's turn now

Then

elease 12, fit again, red kites

k easy

Out the back Colin's go

New mum Melanie's turn

Diploma student Danielle has a go next

35 | 36

Sicknote Sarah is next

ool Tim

DIY advisor Lynne has her go

And finally modern man Joe

Believe it or not this diminutive swift
was misidentified as a red kite.

Another Day.

Tiggys' work with red kites seems to grow in importance every day with information being one of the crucial facets of the profile. On one day a phone call about a grounded 'red kite' the other side of HighWycombe. Found in a small garden, unable to fly, the 'kite' is put safely in a box. Tiggys immediately despatched the nearest volunteer rescuer Steve. In no time at all he arrives at the scene and opens the box expecting a large red kite. But no this 'red kite' is a swift, another spectacular flying bird, grounded and too weak to take off. Steve brings it back to base for recuperation and recovery. Just as important an outcome as any other rescue.

Next call almost immediately: a red kite has been 'running' between gardens in Watlington, major red kite environment. It was having no success in trying to fly away from the gardens. This time Les went together with Sue, Lucy and some large nets. As usual on arrival there was no sign of the kite. However gathering a few neighbours into the search we soon found the bird skulking under a large bush. Lucy, with a net moved in. The kite ran only to be confronted with Les and his enormous net. The kite retreated towards Lucy. 'Move in on him', shouted Les and as Lucy dived into the bush the kite made a dash in Les's direction and was deftly contained. For a mysterious reason this red kite had numerous broken flight feathers effectively grounding it.

39 | 40

Back at Tiggys' it was soon realised that too many feathers had been broken. Replacing the feathers was not an option. This red kite would have to stay in until it had moulted out and had a new set of flight feathers to help it on its way. Remarkably the instant Les and his team got back with their kite then another red kite arrived at reception. Found by a gamekeeper this kite turned out to be a perfectly fit youngster that had left its nest too early. Not yet ready to fly it had come to the ground at the mercy of cats, dogs, foxes and even badgers. Luckily he was brought into us and would have to stay for a few weeks until he was competent enough to be released. As is the normal recommended practice we wrapped its tail feathers to prevent them getting damaged while it was in one of our rehabilitation aviaries.

(Left) Injured red kites can often run away and lead a rescuer a 'merry dance'. This is where a long handled net is crucial.

(Right) Les checks the red kits for injury.

Seeming to be in the forefront of red kite rescue, rehabilitation and release in this Country our existing red kite facility, although huge, did not provide enough space and individuality so new facilities had to be built. Referring once more to 'Bright Eyes' the Tiggys' members' newsletter, this article, written by Les aptly illustrates the pride we feel in our bird neighbours:-

"The Special Ones"

Sitting at my desk I am finding it so difficult to concentrate on this information. Why? My desk overlooks the back of the Hospital, the heart of the running of Tiggys. There are the food stores, the workshop, refuse bins, staff car park, washing lines and, most of those vital utilities that keep us ticking over so vibrantly. All that is not very interesting but soaring, acrobatting, squabbling with the crows and looking so awesomely spectacular in the sky are six wild red kites in the bright sunlight. They twist and turn catching the sun in their feathers, their light heads and forever searching piercing eyes. It is impossible not to just watch them and realise how lucky we are to be in the heart of the, so successful, Chiltern's red kite extravaganza. Surely these are Britain's most special birds.

True we now sadly get many red kite casualties. It is fantastic to get so close to them but to come into us, like all casualties, they are close to death. Thankfully being such a large bird we are able to provide intravenous therapy and if necessary sophisticated orthopaedic surgery and get the vast majority into our rehabilitation and release programme.

(Right) Wild red kites visiting Tiggywinkles.

Victims of our own success, our specially built red kite aviary has in a few years become stretched to the limit with convalescing casualties, recovered casualties exercising before release as well as those not quite 100% and not fit enough to be released. Being Tiggys we always strive to provide the best, in our opinion, that our patients need. We have built a specialised facility we call the National Red Kite Rescue, Rehabilitation and Release Centre. There are three new giant aviaries, one of each to cope with the three categories of patients; convalescing, being released and living here. Our fantastic members and supporting visitors are able to see our work with red kites, of course, if the birds don't mind. We have also to open a brand new Red Kite Information Centre with all the gen on these wonderful birds. There is also available all manner of red kite-abilia (terrible word – but apt) And-and-and those six red kites I am watching will probably keep up those daily visits so everybody can stand and marvel at "The Special Ones", the Red Kites.

P.S One has just landed in a small tree – sorry I can't concentrate to write anymore!

Wild red kites visiting Tiggywinkles.

The new Tiggywinkles' red kite facility with three giant rehabilitation aviaries and an information centre.

Details of Tiggywinkles Wildlife Hospital
Registered Charity No. 286447

The Aims and Objects of Tiggywinkles are providing, maintaining and staffing a permanent free medical facility designed to cater for all species of British wild birds and other animals.

In furtherance of these aims Tiggywinkles provides support and education on the subject of wildlife rescue, rehabilitation and release together with general animal welfare through publications and courses.

In support of further education and clinical pathology monitoring, the Trust is working closely with university and government agencies.

Tiggywinkles also works closely with European and other international centres in the exchange and support of relevant information.

Tel: 01844 292292
Fax: 01844 292640
Email: mail@sttiggywinkles.org.uk

Tiggwinkles'
Aston Road
Haddenham
Bucks
HP17 8AF

www.tiggywinkles.com

Other books available by Les Stocker

Practical Wildlife Care - Second Edition. Blackwell Publishing. 2005
Something in a Cardboard Box - Chatto and Windus. 1989
The Complete Fox - Chatto and Windus. 1994
We save Wildlife - Animal Images. 1994
Jaws, the Smallest Badger in the World and other Stories - Harper Collins. 1998

Obtainable on www.tiggywinkles.com